THE GENERAL INFIRMARY AT
A PICTORIAL HIST

Front cover: *the Gilbert Scott Building.*   Back cover: *the Jubilee Wing.*

To

THE PHOTOGRAPHERS

who recorded the development of

The General Infirmary

at Leeds

The General Infirmary at Leeds

A Pictorial History

Malcolm Parsons

Formerly Consultant Neurologist at The Infirmary

William Sessions Limited
York, England

ISBN 1 85072 300 1

Printed in 10 point Plantin Typeface from Author's Disk
by Sessions of York
The Ebor Press, York, England

Contents

List of Illustrations

Preface

IN 1771 A NEW HOSPITAL was opened in Leeds. The following year a vast and ancient hospital was destroyed by fire in Paris. The events were of course entirely unrelated, but in due course plans to rebuild the latter precipitated a revolution in hospital design. A century later, when the Infirmary at Leeds was itself rebuilt, this new approach was adopted. The result was a building which, from an artistic and scientific point of view, is a landmark in the design of British hospitals.

The story of the General Infirmary at Leeds has already been told in great detail by Dr. S.T. Anning in two volumes published in 1963 and 1966, and it would be almost impossible to add anything of significance to his excellent narrative. It is however interesting to look in a little more detail at the sequence of events that led to these developments. Moreover, after thirty-five years there is perhaps scope for a companion volume to record the changing fortunes of the Hospital since the second book was published. But the main purpose of this book is to bring together some of the remarkable illustrations that trace the development of the Infirmary and its surroundings and to 'let the pictures (which, on close inspection, contain an amazing amount of information) tell the story'.

The history of hospital design in the eighteenth century has recently been described in great detail by Christine Stevenson, and I have made extensive use of her excellent book *Medicine and Magnificence*. In following the recent history of the Infirmary I have relied on the *History of the Leeds School of Medicine* by Dr. S.T. Anning and Dr. W.K.J Walls, the 1965 *Grey Book* which outlined the plans for the 'new hospital' that was never built and various brochures, circulars and press releases collected over the years. I must also express my gratitude to the Special Trustees of the Infirmary, to the Leeds Library and Information Services and the Leodis Project of the Leeds' Libraries who allowed me to examine and reproduce pictures from their archives, to Dr. Aleck Brownjohn, Mr. R Hughes-Rowlands M.B.E., Mr. K R Peel and the late Professor R W Smithells who kindly read the manuscript and made helpful suggestions and to Mr. Bob Sissons and Mr. Andrew Lee of Sessions who have so successfully converted a mass of disparate illustrations into a readable text. Above all, however, I would like to thank the many photographers whose work forms the basis of the book. Their names, sadly, are not recorded but the pictures are a lasting tribute to their skill.

Malcolm Parsons
January 2003

Morning Prayers – a ceremony which still took place on certain wards in the 1970's.

1 – The First Infirmary

THE HOSPITAL MOVEMENT in England was a product of the Industrial Revolution. Up to this time the predominantly rural population had been well fed and healthy, but in the eighteenth century it enlarged and migrated into towns. Here both living and working conditions were atrocious, and the task of dealing with those who were sick and injured soon became a matter of urgency. It was of course a problem that concerned the philanthropists, who added it to their many other worries about contemporary society. But it was of more direct interest to two other groups. The first was the employers – not only of workers in industry but also of the army of domestic retainers on whose services polite society depended. Apart from being anxious to get their employees back to work, they had the problem of knowing what to do with them while they were ill. They would therefore have been interested to read in the first Annual Report that 'by the advantage of an Infirmary, many patients will probably soon be restored to the strength and Capacity of Labour', for at that time the right to refer patients to a hospital was vested in the hands of its lay supporters. But the idea of an Infirmary was also of interest to certain members of the medical profession, for apart from enhancing their status in society it allowed them to segregate a group of patients who could be studied and treated out of sight of interfering relatives. This was but one manifestation of a growing belief that the poor should in some way repay their debt to society – a belief that was quite openly expressed. As one 1767 textbook of surgery

Fig. 1.1). *Mr. Wilson's House in Kirkgate, the first building in Leeds used by the Infirmary.*

1

explained, 'hospitals funded by voluntary contributions have a direct tendency to promote and perfect knowledge of this art, making the benefit extend to all ranks of people'. (The extension was, of course, upwards!) A German professor was even more direct, pointing out that 'the hospital is not there to serve the patient, but the patient the hospital'. This was an attitude of which the general public was well aware although its response, naturally, was somewhat variable. Speaking for the aristocracy one of George Eliot's characters observed that he 'had no objection if you like to try a few experiments on one of your hospital patients and kill a few people for charity. But I am not going to hand money out of my purse to have experiments tried on me'. The lower orders, understandably, saw matters in a somewhat different light and quickly decided that hospitals were 'schools of medicine where practitioners make experiments on the poor to improve themselves in the art of treating the rich'. The Trustees, by contrast, had no doubts about the benefits bestowed, and patients who had been discharged but failed to give thanks for their cure at the Parish Church were hauled before the Board. The misgivings of clients were swept aside, and those who refused admission were deemed to be of a 'timorous Disposition and weak Spirit, having a false Fear of undergoing such necessary Operations, as had been the

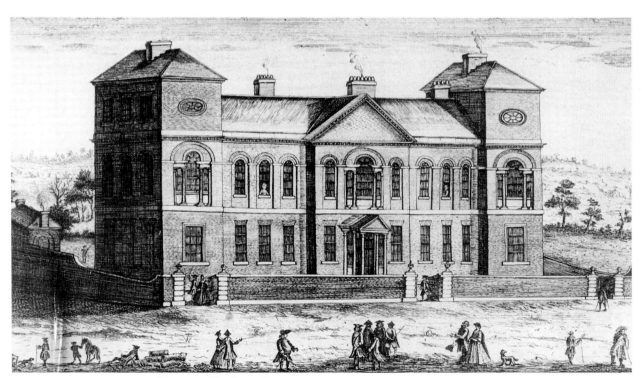

Fig. 1.2). *The first Infirmary (1771) in its original, two-storey form.*

Means, in similar cases, of restoring many of their Families and Friends, and, in all human Probability, would have effected their Cure'. With the benefit of hindsight, one wonders if the patients might not have been rather more perceptive.

Be that as it may, hospitals there had to be and in 1767 a group of local worthies, like their contemporaries in other English towns and cities, gathered in the New Inn (opposite what used to be Dysons' on Briggate) to plan one for Leeds. Among the results of their deliberations was the decision that the establishment should be called The General Infirmary at Leeds. The words were carefully chosen. It was *at* Leeds but not, unlike the Workhouse, exclusively *for* Leeds. It was moreover an *Infirmary* and not a hospital – ie it was 'for the cure of the sick' and not an alms-house or even (like Christ's Hospital) a school. This meant that, as in many similar institutions, the statutes forbade the admission of 'women big with child, children under six years of age (except with fractures, or where Cutting for the Stone or operation is required), Persons disordered in their Senses, and those suspected to have the Small-Pox, Venereal Disease, Itch or other infectious Distempers, that are apprehended to be in a Dying Condition, or incurable'. Subsequently those with 'epileptic fits, habitual ulcers

Fig. 1.3). *The Infirmary after the addition of a third floor and 'wings' in 1792. The church in the background is St. Paul's Park Square – now demolished.*

3

and consumption' were added to this list and it was specified that if any such were 'inadvertently admitted they should not be suffered to continue'. It was also decreed that if, after two months, patients had not been cured they should be discharged – a regulation which led to Mr. Lucas being asked why his patient Mary Walker, admitted on February 11th., 1791 was still in the hospital in March 1792. It was no doubt with some satisfaction that he informed the Board that it was a different Mary Walker, and that in any case she wasn't his patient!

The project started in a house in Kirkgate – long since demolished – which belonged to a Mr. Andrew Wilson (Figs. 1.1) and it was not until 1771 that the first Infirmary was opened 'to the great joy of every benevolent heart; on which pleasing occasion the lower ranks of the people testified their gratitude by ringing of bells'. Designed by John Carr, architect of Harewood House, it cost about £5,000 and stood in virtually open country on the salubrious west side of the town on the site now occupied by the Yorkshire Bank in Infirmary Street (Fig. 1.2). Naturally, like all new hospitals, it had its problems. The foundations were deemed to be inadequate and had to be rebuilt; the chimneys smoked; the drains gave trouble and the water supply was

Fig. 1.4). *A photograph of the rear of the original Infirmary (showing the additional 'wings') taken in 1867 shortly before it closed. The Retreat or Garden Ward is thought to have been a psychiatric ward – like the Retreat at York.*

unreliable. But eventually, in the opinion of the philanthropist John Howard, it proved to be 'one of the best hospitals in the kingdom' and one which even contrived to control infection, the great bane of such institutions, with the result that 'many are here cured of compound fractures who would lose their limbs in the unventilated and offensive wards of some older hospitals'. In general, however, it was unremarkable, and despite a series of extensions which increased its capacity from 27 to 150 beds (Fig.1.3, 4) it eventually became evident that both it and the site were too small. In 1869 the Infirmary was therefore moved to its second (present) building, once more on the outskirts of the town, behind the new Town Hall. The old site, which had nearly been requisitioned to build a railway station in 1845, was in fact sold to the North Eastern Railway Company. In the event, however, it was not used by them and, after serving among other things as a Public Library, it was eventually demolished in 1893 to make way for the Yorkshire Penny Bank (Fig. 1.5).

Fig. 1.5). *The demolition of the original Infirmary in 1893.*

5

2 – The Gilbert Scott Hospital

A S IT STRUGGLED TO cope with the growing population of Leeds and the West Riding the number of beds in the Infirmary had risen from 27 to 150. But at one stage the number of in-patients reached 171 and by the latter part of 1858 it was evident that further expansion was required. The Board was therefore faced with a difficult decision. On the one hand it did not wish to abandon the existing building and move up the hill away from its main catchment area and the station. On the other, this was the last opportunity to expand on the existing site and even so the new wards, contrary to current teaching, would only have windows on one side. Over the next three years various plots and plans were therefore considered until eventually, in January 1862, it was decided to erect a new three hundred bed hospital on the present site in Great George Street. This decision was to produce a building that, from a scientific, technological and artistic point of view, was a landmark in hospital design. The full significance of the development can only be understood, however, if for a moment we digress to consider the history of hospital design in the United Kingdom and in France.

English Hospitals

Following the dissolution of the monasteries in the 16th century England had been left without a hospital service. The aged and destitute were cared for – or at any rate housed – in alms- and work-houses, but those who were sick were treated in their own homes. It was not therefore surprising that when hospitals started to appear they, like the Infirmary, were accommodated in what had been, or at any rate looked like, private houses. Sadly it soon became evident that this was a mistake, for compact buildings in which a family could live in great comfort became death-traps when occupied by a few dozen infected or infectious patients. The main problem was lack of ventilation, and visitors to the first Infirmary were surprised to find that the air in it was 'not in general much less pure and healthy than in private houses'. Few hospitals could make such a claim, and by 1752 military surgeons like Pringle were listing hospitals 'among the causes of sickness and death in the army'. Patients, they found, were much safer if they were housed in barns, tents or even ruined buildings. There were moreover worries about the way in which some hospitals lavished (charitable) money on the external adornments of the building, and even suggestions that a better and less expensive service could be provided on an outpatient and domiciliary basis by the dispensaries. When the first Infirmary opened in 1771 civic hospitals were not, therefore, proving to be an unqualified success. Indeed, in the words of a contemporary French author (admittedly talking about the much larger institutions in France), the hospital was 'a fragment of space closed in on itself, a place of internment of men and diseases, its ceremonious but inept architecture multiplying the ills in its interior without preventing their outward diffusion – more a centre of death for the cities where it is sited than a therapeutic agent for the populace as a whole'.

There was however one area in which a hospital service appeared to be much more satisfactory. In dealing with their vast clientele – for the British Navy was 'by a large margin the largest industrial organization in the western world' – naval surgeons were faced with two problems that did not affect their colleagues in civilian practice. They had to accept large numbers of patients with potentially dangerous fevers and they had to ensure that those patients, many of whom were pressed men, did not escape. Not having enough purpose built hospitals at their disposal they were forced to improvise, and in 1660 they hit on the fortunate idea of using old warships. These hulks, of which the navy always had a generous supply, proved to have three great assets. Anchored in mid-stream they could of course provide the security demanded of a naval hospital. The gun-ports on each side ensured that their 'wards' were at least adequately ventilated. And by distributing patients between the various decks it was possible to isolate those with infectious diseases. It was a fortunate and significant discovery, and by the middle of the 18th. century a quarter of all naval patients were housed in this way.

Even more fortunate was the fact that when the Admiralty eventually decided to build naval hospitals it determined, in one of the earliest pieces of specific hospital design, to replicate these advantageous features. Its first experiment, at Haslar, was completed in 1762. The largest brick-built construction in the country, it was situated on a peninsula where it was safely surrounded by water and by mud. To ensure adequate ventilation its 114 wards were ranged end to end round three sides of an open courtyard in a complex 'U within a U' pattern that allowed all to have windows on both sides. The courtyard itself was surrounded by a cloister in which convalescent patients could exercise, but to ensure isolation individual wards were separated by open walkways. In this way the medical director, James Lind, was able to segregate those with fevers for, as he pointed out, many 'had a limited range of infection' that 'would automatically dissipate if patients were well separated'. It was a successful experiment, and the mortality was in the region of one in fourteen. (The mortality in the Hotel Dieu in Paris – admittedly a different sort of hospital – was one in four). Unfortunately, as the Infirmary was to discover, it was also an expensive one, for construction of threequarters of the original design cost £100,000, two and a half times the original estimate.

In the same year the Admiralty completed a second, even more important hospital at Plymouth with beds for over 1,000 patients. Once more, it was built round three sides of a cloister-lined square. In the centre of the base was a chapel, but it and the ten ward blocks were free-standing, isolated buildings set at right angles to the connecting walk-way. It was in essence the Haslar design, but with the wards uncoupled and rotated through ninety degrees (Fig. 2.1). This layout proved to be even more successful, and mortality fell to a level of one in twenty-five.

French Hospitals

Meantime in France a very different sequence of events was unfolding. The French had retained their monastic institutions and over the years these 'hospitals' had became a repository, not only for the sick, but also for orphans, cripples, the mad, the bad, the destitute, the aged and every other outcast from society. As the population migrated into the cities, buildings like the Hotel Dieu on the Isle de la Citie rapidly became ungovernable. Founded in 660 as part of Notre Dame it had gradually expanded until it now housed 5,000 'patients' – a population larger than that of threequarters of the towns in France. Its buildings had sprawled up one bank, out onto piles over the river, across a neighbouring bridge and down the shore on the opposite side. Conditions in and around its wards, many of which housed up to eight patients in a single bed, were horrendous and in the opinion of one observer the wing on the south bank was 'the most dangerous place on earth'. The fire which destroyed this monstrosity in 1772 was not therefore an unqualified disaster.

Despite contemporary doubts about the value of hospitals the problem of rebuilding the Hotel Dieu attracted considerable interest, for it had both Parliamentary and Royal support. It soon became evident, however, that the extensive literature on architecture contained nothing on the *functional* design of hospitals and that once more the so-called 'experts' were concerned only with the external adornment of the building. The Academie des Sciences was therefore given the task of assessing ideas from other quarters. One ingenious plan envisaged a hospital on the site now occupied by the Eiffel Tower. By cutting a new channel this was to be converted into an island on which a wheel-shaped hospital was to be built. At the hub of the wheel was the chapel, and radiating from it were sixteen blocks of wards that would, of course, have windows on both sides. Drainage was ensured by the flow of the surrounding river and by a large culvert that crossed the site underneath the

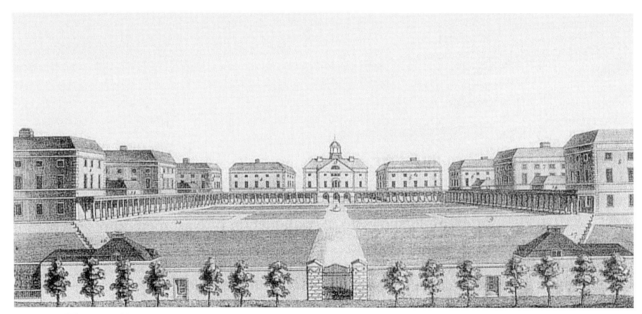

Fig. 2.1). *The Plymouth Naval Hospital (1757) – the first hospital to be built on a (modified) pavilion plan.*

building (Fig. 2.2). It was an idea that clearly addressed many of the problems of ventilation and sanitation that had plagued the old building.

In the event the Academie rejected this suggestion and, in 1788, recommended its own scheme for the construction of four hospitals built on what was to become known as the pavilion plan. In essence this consisted of groups of wards, each with windows down both sides, that would stand side by side as 'individual and isolated hospitals'. The wards were to be lofty because this was known to reduce mortality, and because 'toxic vapours and exhalations' tended to rise, no more than three wards were to be placed one on another. Each hospital would have twelve such blocks (holding 1,200 patients) and these would be set at right angles to the long sides of a cloistered courtyard, with a chapel on one of the short sides. It was a scheme which, as the judges shiftily admitted, bore a striking resemblance to one first proposed in 1773 by the physicist Le Roy, and it was with some satisfaction that they 'discovered' that it had already been implemented at Plymouth twenty-five years earlier. In saying this, however, they were not strictly correct, for although Plymouth had the general appearance of a pavilion hospital one important element was lacking. The wards, instead of having windows down *both* sides, lay side by side in pairs so that each ward only had windows down *one* side. Important though it was in the evolution of hospital design it is not therefore strictly correct to say that Plymouth was the first pavilion-type hospital.

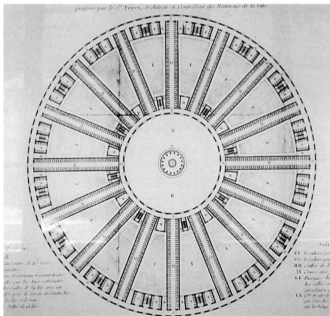

Fig. 2.2). *One of the designs suggested for the rebuilding of the Hotel Dieu, Paris. It consisted of a hub occupied by the chapel and sixteen radiating wards.*

9

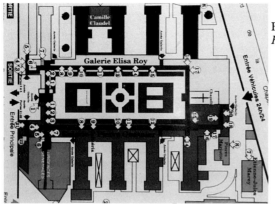

Fig. 2.3). *A plan of the Lariboisiere Hospital, Paris.*

The New Infirmary

By the time the first Infirmary opened, therefore, both England and France had started to adopt the idea of multiple free standing wards – the former on the basis of practical experience and the latter on the basis of logical thought. Developments in France were of course halted by the Revolution – during which an abortive attempt was made to abolish hospitals altogether – and the rebuilding of the Hotel Dieu in this way was delayed for many years. Nevertheless in 1860, when the staff of the Infirmary started to plan a new building, their representatives were able to visit a pavilion-style hospital in Paris, the Lariboisiere.

The similarity between the Lariboisiere and the Infirmary is still immediately apparent, for both consist of a central courtyard with a carriage arch at one end and a chapel at the other. The wards radiating from the sides of the courtyards comply with the teaching that they should be tall and well ventilated, not more than two or three stories high, face east and west and have windows on both sides. The wards are linked by remarkably similar, well lit corridors, but while that in the Lariboisiere is still only one storey high, the one in the Infirmary has subsequently had a

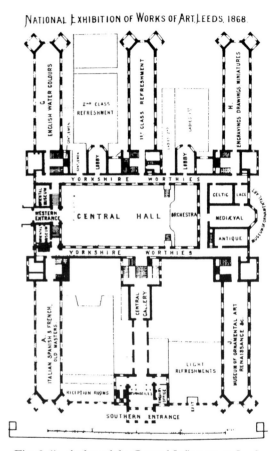

Fig. 2.4). *A plan of the General Infirmary at Leeds set out for the National Exhibition of Works of Art. Note how, as in the Lariboisiere, the wards radiate from the long sides of a courtyard that has a carriage arch at one end and a chapel (marked 'medieval') at the other.*

second storey added to it (Fig. 2.3-8). (When the Academie was assessing the plans for the Hotel Dieu in 1788 the French surgeon Tenon pointed out that, for someone visiting all ten upper wards, the latter scheme avoided 1,344 steps!). The upper wards in the Infirmary were also served by hydraulic lifts, and tradition has it that during the war (when the Brotherton Wing sustained bomb damage on March 14/15, 1941), the hospital's supply of radium was placed for safety each night at the bottom of one of the (now disused) cylinders that powered these lifts*.

The architect of the Infirmary, George Gilbert Scott, had the benefit of the advice of Sir Douglas Galton, who had designed the Herbert Hospital at Woolwich (the only other British hospital built on a pavilion plan) and of Florence Nightingale, whose views on such matters were widely respected. It was Miss Nightingale who advised that the wards should contain about thirty beds – this being the number that one nurse could oversee (Fig.2.9-12). It was also decided that the sluices should be in claw-like extensions at the ends of the wards so that they too should be fully ventilated (Fig. 2.4,14). Sadly Miss Nightingales' knowledge of finance seems to have been somewhat less profound than her knowledge of hygiene, for she too underestimated the cost of a *pavilion* style hospital (£122,329) by a factor of four!

Fig. 2.5). *The courtyard of the Lariboisiere looking towards the chapel.*

---

* This was an improvement on its previous performance, for in 1906 and 1921 the hospital contrived to 'lose' its radium!

11

Fig. 2.6). *An illustration of Scott's Infirmary. In reality the central courtyard was always enclosed while the building was in this form (see 4.1). It does however show the corridor round the courtyard only at first floor level – as in the Lariboisiere (1) A second floor was added at a later date to serve the upper wards (3.7). Note the lantern window of the original theatre (2); the Annual Meeting Room above the front porch (3) which is not, as yet, linked to the main building; the 'claws' for the sluices at the ends of the wards (4); and Mount Pleasant, later the site of the third medical School (5).*

12

The first task was to dispose of a Baptist Chapel on the proposed site. This was purchased from the congregation who built the Blenheim Baptist Chapel with the proceeds, and the building itself was moved and re-erected (with a belfry) as Saint Simon's Ventnor Street – now demolished. Scott was also faced with the problem that, while the Lariboisiere was situated on level ground, the new Infirmary was to be built on a south-facing slope. This meant of course that the wards round the courtyard would be at different levels. To overcome this difficulty he 'wedged' an additional floor under the front of the building, thus raising the two blocks at the front to the same level as the three at the back. (The relative heights of the north west and south west towers shows how essential this was (Fig. 2.13,14) The extra floor was used to provide a casualty department, mortuary, kitchen, store, accommodation for medical staff, a board room and a fine hall leading to the main staircase (Fig. 2.15-17). The one drawback of this design is that – to this day – visitors entering the back of the

Figs. 2.7,8). *The main corridor of the Lariboisiere (left) and of the Infirmary (right).*

13

Fig. 2.9). *One of the upper wards during the National Exhibition of Works of Art.*

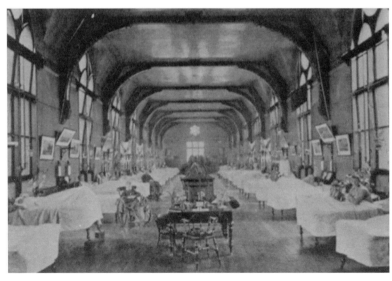

Fig. 2.10). *A similar ward in use in 1902. The excellent ventilation and illumination produced by the high-arched roof and the tall windows were sadly missed when the ceiling was lowered in the process of 'modernisation'. It was however found that the stove (foreground) did not provide enough heat to warm the ward.*

Fig. 2.11). One of the lower wards in use about 1909. Note that the tops of the windows and the beams are horizontal and that the design of the end window is less elaborate.

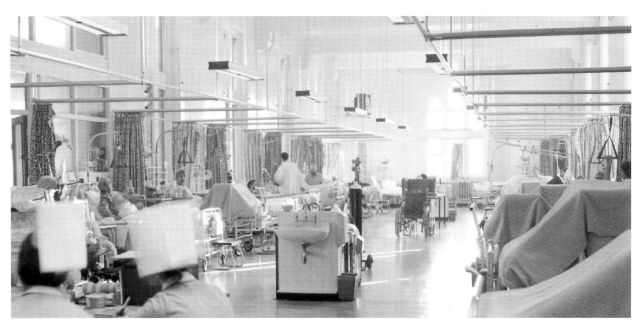

Fig. 2.12). A similar ward in use in about 1975.

15

Figs. 2.13,14). *The ends of the north-west and south-west ward blocks to show how an extra floor has been inserted at the front of the hospital to compensate for the sloping site. The difference in the design of the windows is again visible.*

16

building at ground floor level are unable to understand how, on going to the front, they have arrived on the first floor.

Quite apart from its scientific and technological excellence, however, the new Infirmary was a sumptuous building. Scott had just completed his masterpiece at St. Pancras Station, and the façade of the Infirmary, the portico and the great 'railway arch' that originally enclosed the courtyard are very reminiscent of this building (Fig.2.18-21). The quality of the workmanship throughout is outstanding, from the corbels supporting the arches in the front hall (Fig. 2.23), each of which is carved to depict a different plant used in medicine (along with the occasional frog and snail), through to the stonework around windows at the back of the hospital that is barely visible from ground level (Fig 6.28). In every respect the final product was indeed one of the

Fig. 2.15). The *Board Room.*

Fig. 2.16). *The front hall during the National Exhibition of Works of Art.*

Fig. 2.17). *Detail of the front hall and main staircase and of the Moynihan bust. Sadly, the fine uniforms are no longer in use.*

foremost hospitals in Europe. It must however be admitted that, for a charity, it failed to accord with the precept that 'magnificence announces too much money in the foundation, or too little economy in the administration'.

The new Infirmary was finally opened in May 1868 at a ceremony in the covered courtyard presided over by the Prince of Wales. This was followed by a concert conducted by Charles Halle. Thereafter the wards and corridors were used to house a National Exhibition of Works of Art (Fig. 2.9, 16, 20). The objective was, of course, to raise money but although half a million visitors attended over the next six months it eventually ran at a loss. Once the exhibition had closed the complicated task of transferring patients and equipment to the new hospital began. This was greatly assisted by various local firms which donated an ambulance and provided cabs, produced inventories and organised sales of unwanted equipment free of charge. Eventually in May 1869 the first patient, a man with a fractured thigh, was admitted and presented with a bible 'suitably inscribed'. His comments are not recorded!

Figs. 2.18, 19). *The porticos of St. Pancras Station and of the Infirmary.*

Fig. 2.20). *The ceremonial opening by the Prince of Wales in the (then covered) central courtyard.*

Fig. 2.21). *The central courtyard before the roof was removed and a second floor was added to the surrounding corridor.*

Fig. 2.22). *The Infirmary Chapel of St. Luke. The carved oak pulpit, given by Mrs. William Gott, has been removed. The suggestion that this building, which was erected by public subscription, was reserved for the use of one denomination nearly resulted in litigation. Even an attempt to use hospital funds to purchase a surplice resulted in a complaint from the Society of Friends.*

Fig. 2.23). *One of the corbels in the front hall, each of which depicts a different plant used in medicine.*

3 – The Growth of the New Hospital

IT WAS THE INTENTION of those who built the new Infirmary that it should 'be equal to the wants of the City a century hence as well as being a credit to the present generation'. The latter objective was certainly achieved, but the planners had no means of knowing that within 50 years the population of Leeds would double. Thus it was that within forty years of the opening 'an expert with special experience of hospitals' was already suggesting that the Infirmary 'should be rebuilt on a new and greatly extended site in one of the suburbs'. This was a suggestion which, over the years, was to be repeated many times. It has yet to be accepted, with the result that Gilbert Scott's building is now surrounded by a motley mass of extensions.

Fig. 3.1). *The original Gilbert Scott building, to show how it was surrounded by roads.*

23

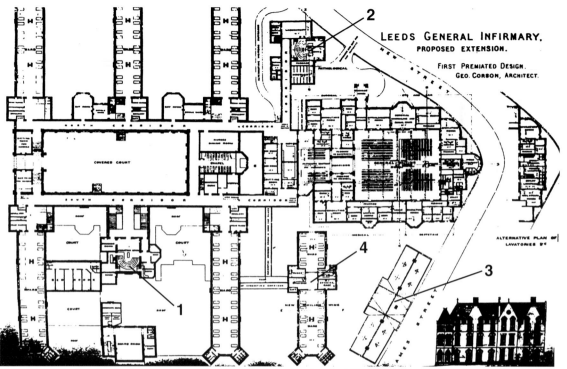

Fig. 3.2). *Corson's plan for the first extension. Note how Thoresby St. (marked New Street) – which originally ran down the east side of the Infirmary – has been diverted; the similarity between the size of the operating theatre (1) and the post-mortem room (2); the way in which the isolation block (3) was originally intended to be at the front of the hospital; and the division of the new wards (4).*

The first extension

It was of course true that the Infirmary was closely invested on all sides by public roads (Fig. 3.1) but in 1892 some extra space was obtained by diverting Thoresby St., the street which ran directly down its east side, so that it ran obliquely south east to Saint James' Street (New St. Fig. 3.2). This allowed the first major extension, carried out by the architect George Corson at the cost of £48,671 (on this occasion a mere three times the original estimate). It included an additional block of wards, an outpatient department, a pathology department and an isolation block (Fig 3.3-5).

The **wards** formed a third block at the front of the hospital which, at first sight, looks exactly like the original two. Closer inspection, however, shows that it contains an additional ward at lower ground floor level, making a bank of three rather than two. Moreover each of these wards was originally split into two sections by

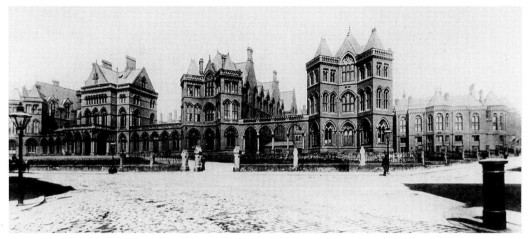

Fig 3.3). *The new (1892) ward block and outpatient hall.*

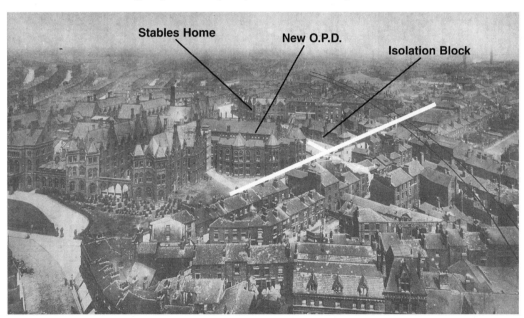

Stables Home

New O.P.D.

Isolation Block

Fig. 3.4). *The new building from above. Note how the Stables Nurses' home and the isolation block face the outpatients' building across the now-diverted Thoresby St. Note also the blinds over the shops in the foreground. The white lines mark the junction of Thoresby St. and St. James's St.*

Fig.3.5). A most instructive picture, taken in 1914, looking downwards and to the right from what is now the entrance to the Martin wing. The shops at the end of the road (St. James's St) still stand at the junction of Great George St. and Portland St. On the right are the entrance to Sunny Bank St., the end of the Isolation Block, Thoresby St., the new Outpatients' Hall and the tip of the 'Corson' ward block at the front of the hospital.. The roof on the left is a Baptist chapel which stood on intersection of Sunny Bank St. and St. James's St. (By courtesy of the Leeds Library and Information Service).

offices that formed a 'blister' half way along their length (Fig 3.2, 6). When, at a later date, they were converted to 'ordinary' Nightingale wards, these 'blisters' became sets of side-wards★. In 1910 the roof of this ward block was destroyed by fire (Fig 3.6) and, having seen how quickly patients could be evacuated along a walkway leading to the roof terrace round the courtyard, a link block was inserted during reconstruction so that the pavilion was fused to the main building. At about the same time the arched roof over the courtyard was removed and the surrounding terrace was lowered to ensure that the upper wards of the Gilbert Scott building had a similar fire escape. This terrace – on which people can be seen on Fig. 3.20 – was subsequently enclosed to form the Sunshine Corridor (Fig. 3.7).

★ It also explains why, on the old nomenclature, these wards were numbered 14/16/18 - having assimilated 15/17/19 which 'disappeared'.

The **outpatient department** stood behind the new block of wards (Fig.3.3-5). Among other things it was needed to house the Ear and Eye department, acquired when the Ear and Eye Infirmary in Park Lane was incorporated in 1870. (The two specialties separated in 1911). The outpatient department was linked to the corridors on the north and south sides of the courtyard and had an outside entrance from the north. It has – with some justification – been likened to a medieval cathedral (Fig. 3.8-10). The immense roof is supported on huge granite pillars, some of which can still be seen on the north side of the main corridor, and it was lit by clerestorey windows. Around the east end was a series of apse-like consulting, examination and operating rooms which give a strange mulberry-like appearance to that end of the hall. They are visible on the plans and on the building itself and can still be traced in the curved walls of staircases in this part of the building. One 'tower' remains at the north east corner of the Wellcome Wing, and can be seen immediately to the right through the window opposite the Edward VII plaque on the main corridor (Fig. 6.19). The 'nave' itself, however, has vanished from sight, the hall having been divided into two floors.

Behind the outpatient hall was a **Pathology Department**. This is only of interest because the post mortem room – perhaps significantly – is every bit as large as the operating theatre then in use (Fig. 3.2). This plan also shows that Corson

Fig. 3.6). *The fire that destroyed the roof of the new ward block in 1910. The projection half way along these wards, which originally contained offices and is peculiar to this block, is well shown on the right.*

27

Fig. 3.7). *The central courtyard after the removal of the roof and the erection of a first floor 'Sunshine corridor' (note change in brickwork at first floor level).*

Fig 3.8). *The cathedral-like great hall of the 1892 extension that replaced the (covered) courtyard as a waiting area for patients.*

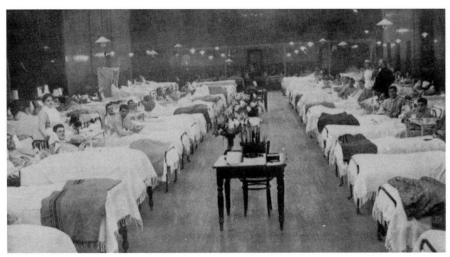

Fig 3.9). *The great hall in use as a military ward during the First World War.*

Fig. 3.10). *The roof of the great hall shortly before it disappeared from view during alterations.*

intended to build the **Isolation Block** alongside the new block of wards at the front of the hospital. In fact this idea was rejected, the building being placed alongside the Stables home on the far side of Thoresby Street and linked to the main hospital by an underground corridor that ran from the lower ground floor of the hospital. (Figs. 3.4, 11).

The Eastern Front

At this stage those who are interested may like to spend a little time examining the road-works and demolition that took place to the east of the hospital during this and the subsequent extension – changes which can be followed in detail on contemporary photographs and from the position of certain strategically placed buildings. Initially, Thoresby St. ran down the eastern flank of the Infirmary from Fenton St. to the junction between

Fig. 3.11) *The Isolation block, which in 1911 became the Department of Venereology. Originally on the far side of Thoresby St. (Fig. 3.4) it was demolished to make way for the Martin wing in 1961. Its position and its distinctive shape make it an invaluable landmark when studying developments in this part of the site.*

30

Fig. 3.12). *The north end of Calverley St., 1908. The Town Hall is on the left and the offices of the Leeds' Education and Schools' Board on the right. In the centre is property on the north side of Great George St. which was demolished (along with many buildings beyond) to extend Calverley St. to Fenton St. (By courtesy of the Leeds Library and Information Services).*

Great George St. and Portland Street. At the north end a side road – Sunny Bank – ran to the east behind what is now the Stables Nurses' Home. A little further down a second branch – Sunny Bank *Street*, followed the line of the road in front of the nurses' homes before turning down through the area occupied by the Martin Wing and running to the south-east border of what is now Millennium Square (see map). A second, larger road (St. James's St.) ran north-east from the junction of Great George St. and Portland St. across Sunny Bank St. and into what is now Portland Way behind the Civic Hall. The lines of these roads can be seen on Fig. 3.4.

To undertake the development just described, the northern part of Thoresby St. had to be diverted so that it ran below and parallel to Sunny Bank St. into St. James's St. This created an island bounded by Thoresby St. on the south, Sunny Bank St. on the north and St. James's St on the east, and it was on this island that the Isolation Block – an invaluable marker – was built. It is visible on Fig. 3.23, marked 2, although St. James's St. – which ran from Portland Way to the junction of Great George St. and Portland St. – has to be imagined. There is however an excellent contemporary picture of the eastern end of this 'island' on Fig. 3.5. The second home for nurses – the Stables Home – was also built on the far side of Thoresby St., in line with the Isolation Block but separated from it by the origin of Sunny Bank St.

In 1911 and 1914 two further appeals were made which between them raised £121,544. The intention was to build another extension to commemorate the reign of Edward VII who, as Prince of Wales, had opened the main Gilbert Scott building. It was however admitted that 'further building on this congested area is much to be deprecated, but it seems difficult to propose any satisfactory plan for extending the accommodation of the Hospital by creating more buildings which would be separated by public streets from the original Infirmary'. In the same year, however, the Chairman, Mr. Charles Lupton, contrived to purchase a large patch of land behind the Stables Home to the north east of the Infirmary (the Sunny Bank site, now occupied by nurses' homes and the boiler house). Soon after the council agreed to extend Calverley Street from the east of the Town Hall to Fenton Street and to sell the land between the new road and the Infirmary to the hospital.

This was a massive undertaking, for at this time the northern limit of Calverley St. was the Town Hall. The north side of Great George St. was built up (Fig. 3.12) and beyond that the new road would have to cross Portland St., St. James's St., Sunny Bank St. and many lesser roads (see map). All were demolished in a vast undertaking that took the extension of Calverley St. in a wide sweep round the existing estate and the land that the Infirmary had just acquired. Fig. 3.20 in particular shows how the Isolation Block and the Stables Home – recently 'on the other side of the street', now sat well inside the Infirmary site, leaving room for the 1917 Edward VII extensions and – sixteen years later – the Brotherton Wing (Figs. 3.13-16).

The King Edward VII Extension

There now occurred one of the most tragic events in the story of the Infirmary – an episode which is barely mentioned in the official history. It was intended that, in addition to accommodation for nurses and a boiler house on the northern part of the new site, the extension should provide new operating theatres and a fourth block of wards at the front of the building. But a far-sighted architect, Mr. E.T. Hall, correctly antici-pating that there would be a continuous demand for more beds, produced a plan which, in the fullness of time,

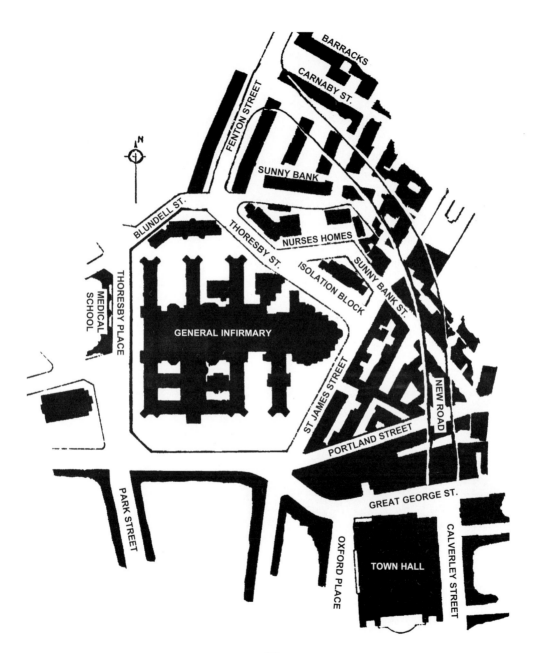

Fig. 3.13). *The extension of Calverley St. 1914 (looking south). A way has been driven through Great George St. and Portland St. and the houses beyond have been demolished (cf. 3.4). The fencing across the centre is along the line of Sunny Bank St. Portland Crescent can be seen on the left. (By courtesy of the Leeds Library and Information Services).*

Fig. 3.14). *The extension of Calverley St. 1914 (looking north). The Outpatients' Hall can be seen on the left and the Isolation Block and the Stables Home can just be discerned in the haze beyond. (By courtesy of the Leeds Library and Information Services).*

Fig. 3.15). *The Calverley St. extension, 1915, seen from Great George St. (By courtesy of the Leeds Library and Information Services).*

Fig. 3.16). *Calverley St 1914. The Outpatients' Hall can be seen over the roof and chimneys of the Isolation Block. To the left of that is the land cleared for the 1917 and (later) the Brotherton Wing developments. (By courtesy of the Leeds Library and Information Services).*

would have provided *three* extra blocks at the front, similar in design to those already in existence. He also advocated the purchase of the plot of land bounded by Great George Street, Portland Street and Calverley Street which was to be converted into a garden. This scheme, which would immediately have provided 100 additional beds and eventually given the Infirmary a truly magnificent frontage, would have cost £100,000 (£50,000 for the land). (Fig. 3.17,18). Sadly, for reasons which are not evident, it was rejected and in 1917 a nondescript new block of wards, designed by Kitson and Parish, was opened (Figs. 3.19,20). A third (isolation block) floor was added in 1937 (compare Figs. 3.23 and 3.24) and in 1940 a new x-ray department was built

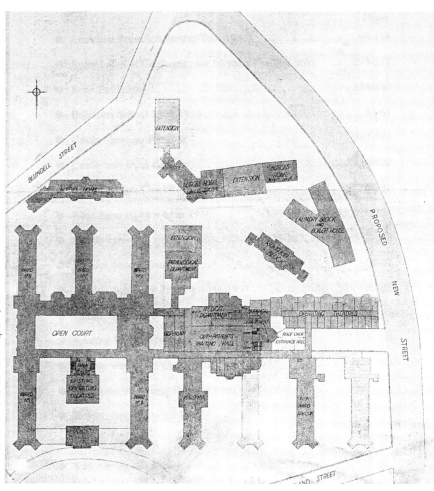

Fig. 3.17). *A 1910 plan – which was not used – that made provision for* three *new ward blocks to match those already built. It also shows the line of the proposed new road (Calverley St.) that brought the Stables Home and the Isolation block onto the main site. (The plan of the nurses' homes is incorrect in that the northern extension runs off the middle section that joins the Stables Home to Sunny Bank House. The boiler house was built at the northern tip of the site).*

on the roof of the theatres (Fig. 3.25). Perhaps the most memorable feature of this Edward VII extension was the provision of a new ophthalmic department by the cricketer Prince Ranjitsinhji, who had been operated on by a member of the staff when his eye was injured in a shooting accident. He continued to make a gift of 100 guineas annually on his birthday until his death in 1932 (Figs. 3.21).

In 1922 the Princess Mary (infants') ward was built between wards eight and ten.

The Brotherton, Martin and Wellcome Wings

In 1933 the eastern flank of the Infirmary underwent a dramatic change with the appearance of the gleaming Civic Hall on the far side of the new road (Calverley St., Fig. 3.22,23). Seven years later, in 1940, the Infirmary matched this with an eighth block of wards and an outpatient department built in a similar style (Fig.

Fig. 3.18). *An artist's impression of how the Infirmary might have looked from the roof of the Town Hall had this plan been implemented. Note the garden produced by demolishing the 'island' of buildings in front of the Infirmary. (1 = Town hall; 2 = Future wards; 3 = New wards; 4 = Garden; 5 = Theatre block).*

Fig. 3.19). *The new (1917) ward block and theatres as they eventually appeared (1). The Isolation block – later to be rebuilt as an extra floor on this extension – is just visible behind the L shaped theatre block (2). Behind this are the Stables Home (3), the 1915 King Edward VII extension (4) and, on the extreme right, the Sunny Bank home in its original 'short' form (5). The end of St. James's St. (now Portland Way) can be seen just above the four-storey building on the right of the picture. Note also the spire on St. George's Church. Despite the apparent lack of traffic the Infirmary was already dealing with 410 road accidents annually in 1924.*

Fig. 3.20). A picture, probably taken in 1922, which shows (moving backwards on the right), the new 1917 ward block, the new L-shaped theatre block, the Isolation ward and the nurses' homes all enclosed by the new road (Calverley St.). The Stables home, the Edward VII home and Sunny Bank house (the last two in their early, 'short' forms) are clearly visible. Note the people on the (as yet uncovered) terrace round the courtyard.

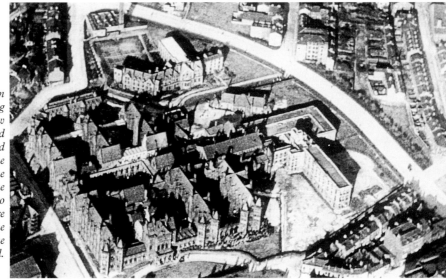

38

Fig. 3.21). *A plaque recording the gift of the eye department by the cricketer Prince Ranjitsinhji, who was attended by one of the staff.*

Fig. 3.22). *The site of the Brotherton Wing opposite the new Civic Hall, opened in 1933. The 1917 ward block still forms the south-east corner of the Infirmary, with the new theatre block behind. Sunny Bank House can be seen below and to the right of the central chimney. (By courtesy of the Leeds Library and Information Services).*

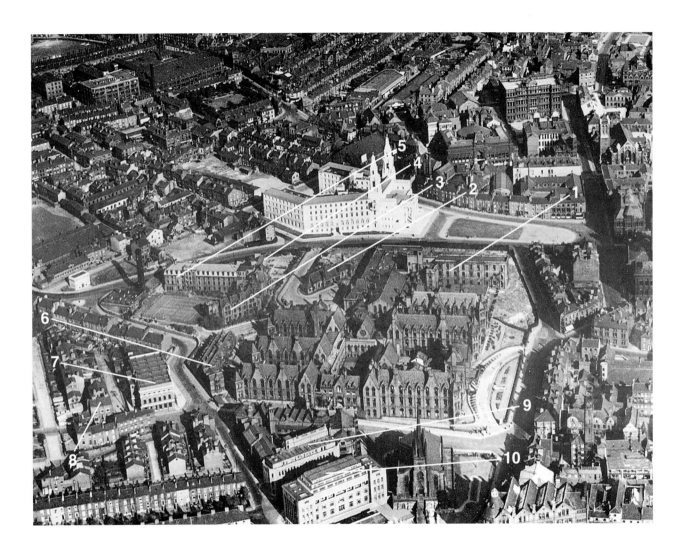

Fig. 3.23). *A photograph taken after the building of the Civic Hall in 1933. 1 = 1917 block; 2 = Isolation Block; 3 = Stables home; 4 = Sunny Bank (demolished); 5 = Edward VII home (enlarged); 6 = Old nurses' home; 7 = Dental hospital; 8 = Tonbridge Hotel; 9 = New wing on medical school; 10 = Algernon Firth building.*

3.24,25). The ward block, which cost £50,000 and now forms the south east corner of the Infirmary, was paid for and named after Mr. **C.F.R.Brotherton**. Elegant enough in itself it is, unfortunately, quite out of keeping with Scott's original design and added to the stylistic jumble that was developing at the front of the Infirmary. Functionally it was much more valuable, for it was designated for patients who were not sufficiently wealthy to afford private (nursing home) treatment but were still sufficiently well off to be ineligible for admission to the public wards. To this end, the fees charged by the hospital and by consultants were limited. It is a matter for regret that the generosity of Mr. Charles Lupton, whose memorial fund paid for the outpatient block, is less well remembered*. In 1973 an additional (Dawson) floor – a long black shed which, luckily, is out of sight – was added to this building. It can be seen as a black line along the roof on Fig. 6.19.

It was to be another thirty-five years before the last two blocks on the main site were in place. These buildings, which were opened within days of each other in 1961, reflected the increasing importance of academic and laboratory medicine. The first, the **Martin** Wing – named after the Chairman of the Board of Governors, Sir George Martin – was designed to accommodate the professorial departments of medicine and surgery and the department of chemical pathology. It ran westwards from the north end of the Brotherton wing, parallel to the front of the nurses' home, and was linked to the main block at the west end by a building paid for by the University. (Fig. 3.26,27). This was the first block to be built with its wards divided into six bed units – a design which has not proved to be universally popular, for privacy is less easy to maintain in a group of six patients than in a group of thirty (3.28). During the course of the construction of the Martin Wing the old Isolation Block (now the Department of Venereology) was demolished.

The second building was the **Wellcome** Wing, which housed the departments of urology and medical physics and an M.R.C. research unit (Fig. 3.29). Like the Martin Wing it was utilitarian in design, and set at the front of the hospital alongside the 1882 block, which had copied Scott's plan faithfully, its appearance can only be described as unfortunate. It was not improved by the addition of an extension at the front which contains a new lift. The disparity between the first three ward blocks and the 1917 block, the Brotherton and the Wellcome Wings is clearly visible on Fig. 3.30, 6.19.

---

* An early occupant of this block was the Department of Dermatology, which introduced the novel idea of outpatient appointments in 1941.

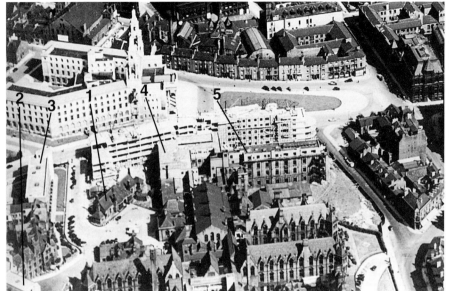

Fig. 3.24). *The building of the Brotherton Wing. After this phase the Isolation Block (1), an important landmark that separated Thoresby Street from Sunny Bank Street, was demolished. Note the new Fenton Street wing (2), Sunny Bank Home (3), x-ray department (4) and isolation ward (5).*

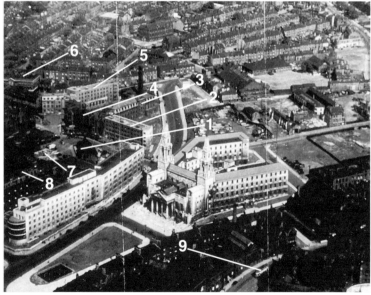

Fig. 3.25). *An overhead view (taken in about 1940) that should be compared with 3.20, 3.23 and 6.19. The Isolation Block stands obliquely behind the new Brotherton wing (1). Above that are the (now elongated) Sunny Bank (2) and Edward VII (3) Homes, the Stables Home (4) and the new Fenton St. wing (5). The Dental hospital (1928) is visible on the extreme left (6). The new x-ray department can be seen on the roof of the theatre block (7) and the new isolation ward on the roof of the 1917 block (8). A Leeds tram is visible in the foreground (9). Note the sea of housing which still surrounds the site.*

Fig. 3.26). *The construction of the Martin Wing, May 1957. The building on the left is the 1917 operating theatre block. The full range of Nurses' Homes is visible on the right.*

Fig. 3.27). *The Martin Wing (1961).*

43

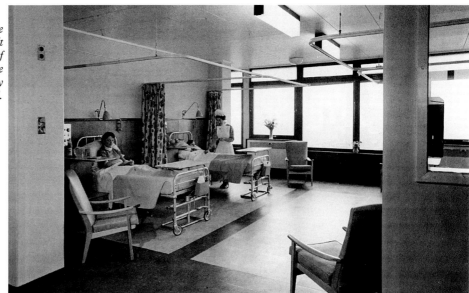

Fig. 3.28). *A ward on the Martin wing, the first to be built with six bedded bays instead of the Nightingale layout. Despite having windows on one side only the lighting was good.*

Fig. 3.29). *The construction of the Wellcome Wing. The site lies between the Corson extension and the 1917 block which is just visible behind the (Town Hall) chimney on the right. Beyond that can be seen the new Martin Wing. Comparison with the virtually identical view on 3.4 shows how much housing has been cleared in the foreground.*

Fig. 3.30). *The four new ward blocks on the front of the hospital – 1892 (1); the Wellcome wing 1961 (before the addition of the new lift – see 6.19) (2); 1917 (3); Brotherton wing 1940 (4).*

4 – The Old Operating Theatres

FROM THE TIME OF its foundation, the Infirmary has been renowned for its surgery and its surgeons. It is therefore surprising that one of its greatest treasures – a set of 19th century operating theatres whose layout is almost intact – should be virtually unknown even within the hospital.

In 1869, when the new Infirmary opened, surgeons were still the second class citizens of the medical fraternity. The introduction of anaesthesia some twenty years earlier had done little to improve their situation,

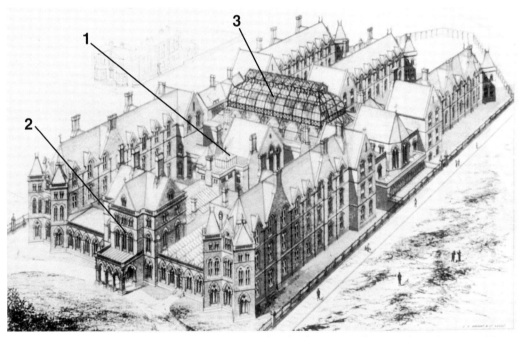

Fig. 4.1). *The Infirmary in its original form, showing the theatre (1), the annual meeting room (2) and the roof over the courtyard (3).*

46

Fig. 4.2). *The entrance to the Littlewood Hall suite -
originally the entrance to the operating theatre.*

Fig. 4.3). *The lobby of the Littlewood Hall suite showing the
lantern window below which the operating table used to stand.
Originally the theatre extended through the facing wall to
include the office beyond. The plaque on the wall commemorates
Harry Littlewood, first Professor of Surgery at the University.*

Fig. 4.4). *The roof light at the front of the old theatre (now an office) with the lantern window beyond.*

for surgical wounds almost invariably became infected and patients who had operations were very likely to die. Nor was this surprising, for at the Infirmary 'the surgical staff operated as a whole, all putting their dirty fingers into interesting wounds and exhaling vapours from their unwashed woollen dressing gowns'. Operations were virtually limited to the amputation of gangrenous or mangled limbs, 'cutting for the (bladder) stone', the couching of cataracts* and the occasional removal of a carcinomatous breast or of an ovarian cyst that had become so large that it was impairing the patient's balance. In 1869 the average number of operations was under one a day, a fifth of them being amputations.

For so small a load, one theatre was sufficient. It can be seen on the well-known birds' eye view of the hospital as a sort of glasshouse on the first floor, a little way behind the front door. (Fig. 4.1). Entrance was via the double doors (now the entrance to the Littlewood Hall suite) in the centre of the landing at the head of the main staircase (Fig. 4.2). The room was the width of the first part of the lobby and the table stood under the lantern window (the 'glasshouse') which still illuminates it (Fig. 4.3). Originally, however, the theatre

---

* ie. pushing the opaque lens out of the line of vision.

48

extended through the facing wall to include the office beyond, in which one can see – behind the false ceiling – a window running up into the roof. From the outside it is evident that this is a roof light to augment the illumination given by the lantern window (Fig. 4.4). The plans show that the patient was confronted almost at once by the table, which was surrounded on the right and beyond by tiers of stands for the students, who entered via a spiral staircase from the hall below (Fig. 4.5).

Antiseptic surgery

While the Infirmary was being built, however, Lister was already toying with the idea that surgical sepsis was due to the invasion of the wound by particles in the air. Having seen carbolic acid used to prevent putrefaction in the rubbish dumps of Carlisle, he hit on the idea of operating under a carbolic spray in the hope of doing the same thing in the theatre. The results were dramatic. His patients were still poor and malnourished and his wards and theatres were still filthy, yet in the year following the introduction of this antiseptic technique many limbs were saved and the mortality among those who did require amputation fell from 45% to zero. 'Nothing of which the world has knowledge', said the distinguished Leeds' surgeon Moynihan, 'has rescued so many lives'. Other colleagues, however, were less easily convinced, and twelve years later Osler, on a visit to the new Edinburgh Royal Infirmary, noted that 'Listerism is not making great headway even in this northern metropolis'. To some extent Lister himself was at fault for, as the British Medical Journal pointed out in 1879, 'there is something, we will not say suspicious but at any rate strange in the persistent avoidance of the challenge thrown out to Mr. Lister and his followers to show, by actual comparison, whether and if so how far his results are really superior'. Soon after, however, his registrar published figures which that same journal admitted were 'so marvellous ..... that they require no comment'.

At least as early as 1866 the Infirmary had started to experiment with this new method and by 1874 the number of operations undertaken had doubled. Between 1875 and 1890 removals of ovarian cysts – virtually the only operation attempted on the abdomen – quadrupled in number with a coincidental fall in mortality from 73% to 15%. To cope with this upsurge in activity more theatre space was required and Corson's plan for the 1892 extension shows how, in 1885, this was accomplished. Rooms on either side of the old theatre were extended. That on the east led into a lobby from which there was an entrance to a new theatre ahead, the old theatre on the right and an anaesthetic room on the left. The west doorway led into a surgeons' room and beyond that there was a room for students entered, as before, from the floor below (Fig. 4.6).

Aseptic surgery

Dramatic though his results had been, by 1880 Lister had realised that the main danger of infection came, not from the air but from fingers and instruments thrust into the wound. Again, his colleagues were slow to accept this idea and as late as 1899 the British Medical Journal, reacting to attacks on conditions in London operating theatres, still found it 'impossible to believe in the high septicity of an English gentleman's fingernails'. Nevertheless, as Treves insisted, 'the secret of surgery was in the nailbrush' – and in other things like linen

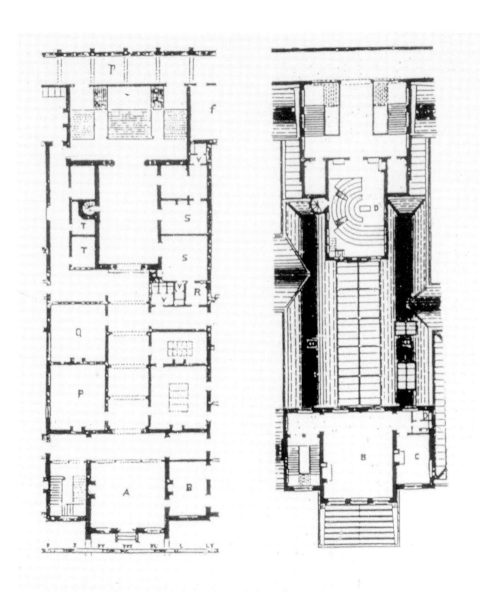

Fig. 4.5). *The plan of the original theatre (right), which lies at the end of the (cross hatched) glass roof of the front hall. Entering from the landing the table is in the centre surrounded on three sides by tiers of stands for students. They enter via a spiral staircase which, as can be seen on the left hand plan, comes up from the ground floor.*

50

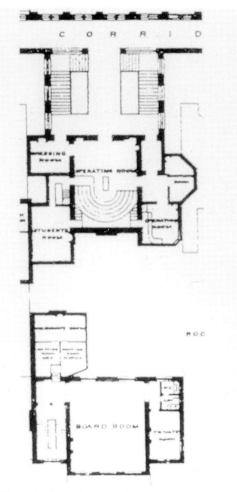

Fig. 4.6). Corson's plan of the 1885 extension. The door at the head of the east (right hand) staircase now leads to a lobby, an anaesthetic room on the right, the old theatre on the left and a new theatre ahead. The door at the head of the west staircase leads to a surgeons' room and beyond that is a room for students. Note also the extension marked microscope room on the west side of the Board Room (Annual Meeting Room).

operating coats to replace the old frock coats, 'so steeped in blood that they could be stood against a wall'. Indeed there seemed to be no end to the sartorial aberrations of surgeons with their gloves, masks, hats and even boots. Gazing with amazement at these last, a visiting Frenchman asked 'Does he stand *in* the abdomen?'

Curious though these accoutrements may have seemed, they (with sterilization) led to a veritable explosion of surgical activity as surgeons were at last enabled to utilise the profound knowledge of human anatomy they had acquired

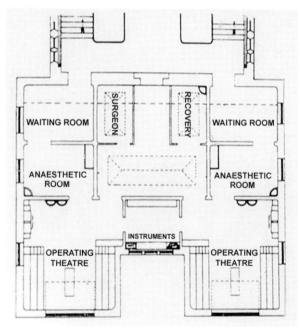

Fig. 4.7). Plan for the 1897 extension. The original theatre is now divided (as at present), the front half being an instrument room. The side doors lead through identical waiting rooms to anaesthetic rooms (now lavatories) and into theatres (now a students' room on the east and a seminar room on the west). The lobby now has additional lantern windows over a recovery room and a surgeons' room on either side of the exit.

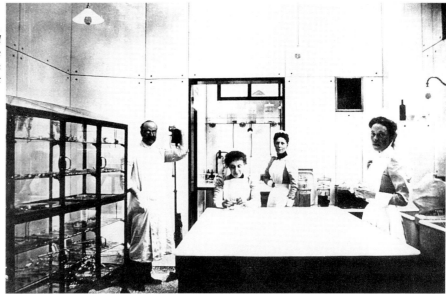

Fig. 4.8). *The instrument room, formed from the front part of the old theatre. The east theatre with its side window is visible through the arch and the window shown on 4.4 is just visible top right.*

Fig. 4.9). *The west theatre, one of a pair built in 1897. Note the south window (now the entrance to the Garland Gallery) and the roof light.*

over the years. In 1897 – a mere twelve years after the first extension – the theatres had to be enlarged yet again. On this occasion identical suites were built on either side of the main entrance. The doors at the top of the staircases led into waiting rooms which in turn led to anaesthetic rooms (now lavatories). These opened into the theatres, now a students' room on the east and a seminar room on the west. The old theatre was split as it is now, the front half becoming an instrument room and the back half a lobby with a surgeons' room on the west and a recovery room on the east (Figs. 4.7,8). Each theatre had a large south window (of which more will be said below) and a roof light which, on the east side, is still visible through the false ceiling of the students' room (Figs. 4.9).

The Annual Meeting Room

The demand for more theatre space continued and within twenty years (in 1917) yet another development took place, producing the fourth set of theatres since the hospital was opened fifty years earlier. It is a measure of the speed with which surgery expanded in those early days that these new theatres – which were part of the Edward VII development and on another site – were to serve the hospital for nearly eighty years. Meantime the old theatres became a teaching block named after Harry Littlewood, the first Professor of Surgery at the University of Leeds.

This development also involved another room about which little seems to be known. The Annual Meeting Room stood above the front entrance (Figs. 4.1, 6) and was not originally connected with the rest of the hospital – being reached via a flight of stairs behind the old Porter's Lodge. Sadly there does not seem to be a

Fig. 4.10) *A strip of plasterwork from the roof of the Annual Meeting Room which remains above the front windows in the corridor that runs across the hospital beyond the Littlewood Hall.*

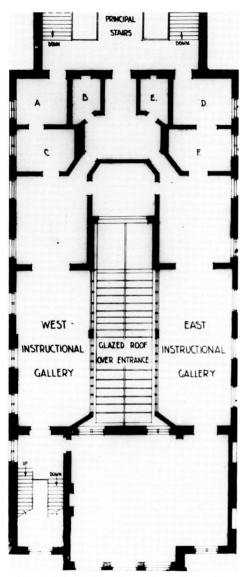

Fig. 4.11). *A plan (date unknown) showing the outline of the 1897 theatres, now with extensions to the Annual Meeting Room.*

picture of it, but from its commanding position, the elaborate strip of plasterwork that remains behind the front windows (Fig. 4.10), a plan which seems to show an ornate fireplace and the fact that it was used for the (very important) meetings of the patrons of the hospital it was probably a fine room. Indeed the only other regular users seem to have been the Leeds and West Riding Medico-Chirurgical society, founded in 1872 – the oldest medical society in Leeds.

It was this society that was responsible for an extension on the north west corner of this room that is marked 'microscope room' on Corson's plans of 1889 (Fig. 4.6) – an interesting indication of how belatedly the medical profession realised the value of this instrument. This room was subsequently extended to produce a connection (now the Garland gallery) with the main hospital via the south window of the west theatre. By 1928 a similar extension (now an office corridor) had appeared on the east side (Fig. 4.11). With the transformation of the Annual Meeting Room into the Littlewood Hall in 1969 the teaching block was complete (Fig. 4.12). But the visitor who climbs the 'ninety nine steps' behind the porter's lodge and looks backwards out of a (kitchen) window can still see all the components of this development. At the end of the glass roof of the front hall is a white structure – the original theatre with its lantern and end windows intact. To right and left are the paired 1897 theatres with their roof lights and ventilation towers. Just visible beyond them are additional roof lights for the rooms on either side of the theatre lobby. And on either side are the extensions from the Annual Meeting Room that run backwards to the walls which once contained the south windows of the twin theatres (Fig. 4.13).

54

Fig. 4.12). *The Annual Meeting Room after its conversion into the Littlewood Hall (1969). The speaker is Professor Sir Ronald Tunbridge. The plaster decoration from the old room is just outside the door on the right.*

Fig. 4.13). *View from above the Annual Meeting Room looking towards the hospital. The original theatre with its roof and lantern windows is in the centre (1). The 1897 theatres with their ventilation chimneys and roof lights stand on either side (2). The lantern windows over the recovery room and surgeons' room are just visible in the angle between the theatres and the (central) landing roof (3). The extensions from the Annual Meeting Room (4) run backwards on either side of the glass roof of the hall (5) to cover the areas once occupied by the south windows of the theatres.*

5 – The Nurses' Homes and Other Surrounding Buildings

THE REMORSELESS RISE IN the demand for beds inevitably led to a request for more accommodation for nurses all of whom, until relatively recently, were resident. Initially the hospital was run by 'a very small, efficient staff of fourteen' which, with the exception of a nurse living in the entresol above the entrance to each ward (Fig. 5.1), was housed above the west entrance to the courtyard. But numbers soon increased and before long it transpired that there were two, three or even four beds in each ill-ventilated room (a serious consideration when tuberculosis was rife) and that there were no facilities for rest or recreation during the day. Nursing, moreover, was undergoing a profound change. Hitherto the Infirmary had relied on 'great, powerful, red-faced women who all ate a great deal of beef and drank a great deal of beer, and lifted the patients as you would lift puppy dogs'. The service they provided was evidently limited, for when Samuel Hey asked the two night nurses at the old Infirmary how they managed if the patients wanted anything he was told 'There isn't a deal of 'em wants owt and if they do they doesn't get it'. But a new sort of nurse was starting to appear, and on hearing that the female attendants at the nearby Wakefield Lunatic Asylum were 'nearly all lightly built, comely looking and dressed after the fashion of the Nightingale Nurses', efforts were made to obtain something similar for the new Infirmary. Lack of space and a desire to improve the purely ward-based training by establishing a

Fig. 5.1). *An entresol - once the home of members of the nursing staff.*

56

Nursing Institution (School of Nursing) therefore led to the building of the first **('old') Nurses' Home.** Situated immediately behind the hospital, this two-storey building, which was designed by Corson and cost £5,000, was opened in 1879. In 1882 a covered way was built between the central entrance of the home and the hospital and a dining room was created, and soon after an extension was added to the west end at the cost of £1,282. (Fig. 5.2). Even so, there is a marked contrast between the stark simplicity of the buildings in which these devoted servants of the Infirmary spent their lives and the sumptuous hospital behind which they are hidden. What happened thereafter is something of a mystery, for in 1891 'plans for the central block of the Nurses' House to be raised two stories' were requested, but 'this scheme appears to have been abortive'. Eventually, however, the work was carried out – possibly in 1925 when 'extensions to the old home' took place (Fig. 5.3).

By 1895 the number of nurses had risen to 85 and once more there were two, three or even four in each room. Further development on the existing site was however impossible, for it was closely invested by roads. These included Thoresby Street which ran south east from Blundell Street, past the east end of the old Home and through what is now the entrance to the Nurses' Home, to join St. James' Street just short of the present site of the Brotherton Wing (see map p.33). In 1895 it was therefore decided to buy the Sunny Bank site on the far side of this road – a large area now occupied by the boiler house and other Nurses' Homes. This area was gradually brought into use. First to appear (in 1898) was the **Stables Memorial Home.** This building, which cost £10,924, stood alongside the Isolation Block on the opposite side of Thoresby Street, being linked to the old Home (which was now used to provide bedrooms) by an underground passage (Fig. 5.4). In 1908 two houses on Sunny Bank Terrace were altered and furnished to create **Sunny Bank House** (Figs.3.19,20) and in 1915 a third block, the **Edward VII Memorial** extension, was built at the cost of £13,868. This linked the Stables and Sunny Bank homes and extended northwards. It was erected in two stages, for maps and photographs show that after 1923 (when Anning, perhaps incorrectly, says the *old* Home was extended) the length of the building doubled (compare Figs. 3.20 and 3.23).

Over the first thirty years of the 20th.century the Hospital grounds therefore contained two separate blocks for nurses separated by what had once been Thoresby Street. The number of nurses had however increased from 93 to 230 and in 1937 these blocks were linked by the new **Fenton Street Wing** which forms the main entrance to the present Home. This crossed the site of Thoresby Street from the old Home to the Stables Home and then ran northwards, parallel to the King Edward building (Fig.5.5). It is best seen by comparing Figs. 3.23 and 6.19. At the same time the old Sunny Bank House, which had been a relatively short building (Fig. 3.20) was demolished (Fig. 3.23) and a new Sunny Bank Wing was erected opposite the Martin Wing (Fig. 3.25, 6.19). Moving from the west the present frontage of the nurses' homes therefore consists of the old Home, the Fenton Street (main entrance) Wing, the Stables home, the King Edward home with its unequal twin gables and the new Sunny Bank Wing.

Looking further afield, the most striking feature of early photographs is the way in which the Infirmary is enveloped in a sea of housing – housing which not only provided it with patients but also with homes for its students (Figs. 3.23). Several prominent buildings can be recognised. To the south west is St. George's Church, which was to lose its spire in a storm. (Compare 3.19 and 6.19). To the north there was the parade ground of

Fig. 5.2). *The old Nurses' Home (1879) before the addition of two extra floors. Note the covered way from the central entrance added in 1882 and the three-bay extension at the west end added in 1885.*

Fig. 5.3). *The old Nurses' Home after the addition of two more floors (? in 1925). Note the change in the colour of the brickwork and the closure of the central entrance.*

Fig. 5.4). *The Stables Memorial Home (1898) before it was joined to other buildings.*

Fig. 5.5). *The Fenton St. Wing (1937) that links the old Nurses' Home with the Stables home, running across what used to be Thoresby St. The metal arch over the entrance in the middle of 5.4 is visible behind the bush on the right.*

Fenton Street Barracks. To the south east stood the Town Hall and, after 1933, to the east there was the gleaming new Civic Hall (Fig. 3.22, 23). This was an appropriate neighbour, as the Infirmary used the arms of the City of Leeds as its crest for 225 years. Less conspicuous but every bit as important were Mr. Finlay's Sandwich Shop and the Tonbridge Hotel which stood just behind the Infirmary (Figs. 3.23, 6.6). With the exception of one room the latter establishment, which slaked the thirst of generations of medical students, was closed to ladies – and the exact status of its few female patrons was said to be questionable.

Over the years other hospital buildings started to appear. The first was the **Medical School.** Founded in 1831 its first long-term home was in No. 1 East Parade – a building which, because it was in a respectable area, the students had to enter by the back door. In 1865 it moved to Park Street (one of the first custom-built medical schools in the country) and in 1894 it moved yet again to the Mount Pleasant site on the west side of the hospital (Fig. 2.6). The hexagonal hall of this fine building bears the arms of Victoria College Manchester, to which the School was affiliated until the University of Leeds got its charter in 1904★.

To the north west was the **Womens' Hospital** (Fig. 6.9). The Hospital for Women and Children in Leeds first opened in East Parade in 1853 and moved to this site in 1861. For many years it had refused to unite with the Infirmary because the latter insisted that all members of staff should be Members or Fellows of one of the Royal Colleges, but amalgamation finally took place in 1909 and in 1913 – after which all children were admitted to the Infirmary – it was known as the Womens' Hospital. Part of the original building still survived, but the majority was built in 1903. It was demolished, with great regret, to make way for the new Medical School in 1974. (The Maternity Hospital, a more functional structure which was recently demolished, was further up Clarendon Road). In 1928 the **School of Dentistry**, which cost £42,000 and was demolished to make way for the Jubilee Wing, appeared to the north of the Infirmary, followed in 1930 by the **west wing of the Medical School** and in 1933 by the **Algernon Firth Laboratories** (Fig.3.23, 6.5).

★ Initially there was opposition to the amalgamation of medical schools and provincial Colleges of Science because medical students, especially in the provinces, were 'intellectually less sensitive and morally coarser than the average student and were a source of potential immorality'.

6 – The Grand Design

AS ONE MOVES INTO more recent years it becomes increasingly difficult to give a balanced history of the Infirmary, for the affairs of the Hospital were becoming entangled with those of other institutions and personal recollections of events may be incomplete or selective. It was, moreover, a period of conflict and setbacks, and as a contemporary member of the staff the author could be accused of bias. Being particularly anxious not to re-ignite disputes which have, at times, separated the two major hospitals I have therefore relied for my information on the official history of the Medical School which, for present purposes, might well be regarded as 'the other side'. The assessment of the results, both architectural and functional, is of course my own.

In essence the sequence of events was this. In January 1962 the Government published a White Paper entitled *The National Health Service: A Hospital Plan* that stated, among other things, that the United Leeds Hospitals (ie the Infirmary and its associated hospitals) were to be rebuilt. In the same year the University, anticipating a rise in the number of students, asked the Board of Governors to participate in the building of a new, integrated medical school and teaching hospital. These, it was emphasised, should provide for an expansion in student numbers, should be 'unified on one site' and should be in close proximity to the University. A Joint Planning Committee was therefore appointed which spent much time and effort in designing a 1,380 bed hospital to meet these requirements. But when the task was completed University authorities refused to accept the plans for the Medical School (as a result of which it was built separately), altered the decision on student numbers (with the result that they could not all be trained on one site) and established a second University Hospital which was not, of course, in close proximity to the University. Meantime the rebuilding of the Infirmary – the Hospital's primary objective – was delayed and, in large part, cancelled and Leeds was left with two underfunded University Hospitals neither of which, for reasons of space and economy, can provide a comprehensive service.

The Plan

This sequence of events started in the 1950s. The Infirmary, parts of which were showing signs of age, was facing the perennial problems of creating more beds and of deciding whether this would best be done on a new, out of town site. Student numbers were not in fact an issue, for the disastrous Willink Report had ordained that there were too many doctors and by 1959 the annual intake of students had fallen from the usual 80 to 53. The University, by contrast, was contending with increasing numbers and was anticipating the effects of the post

61

war 'baby boom'. It was indeed estimated that the number of students would rise from 3,200 in 1953 to more than double that figure by 1970. It therefore commissioned a Development Plan, the results of which were published in 1960.

This plan emphasised the importance of establishing a new Teaching Hospital, Medical School and School of Dentistry at one and the same time if they were to be closely and sympathetically integrated, and strongly recommended that the Inner Ring Road – then under construction – should be covered so that the University and Hospital sites were not divided (Fig. 6.4)*. In the words of the Vice Chancellor it was 'Probably the unique opportunity in this country of replanning the Teaching Hospital and Schools on a site adjoining that of the University. Such a development will strengthen the links not only between the Teaching Hospital and Schools, but between the Schools and the University as a whole'. This was of course an historic link, for it was the union of the Infirmary Medical School (founded in 1831) and the much younger Yorkshire College that eventually led to the foundation of the University of Leeds.

Meantime in January 1962 the Infirmary heard with relief that the Government intended to rebuild the Hospital. In May of that year the Board of Governors and the University therefore set up a Joint Planning Committee and a Planning Team. It so happened that at this time extensive slum clearance was taking place in the area between the University and the Infirmary and in 1965, in an alteration to the City's Development Plan, 43 acres of this land were secured. The Planning Team therefore took on the daunting task of designing a Medical Centre on this site – ie a combination of a new Teaching Hospital, a new Medical School and a new Dental Hospital which could serve the community and (as instructed by the University Grants Committee) train 100 medical and 60 dental students each year. It was 'fundamental to the concept that this training should be carried out in a Centre unified on one site'.

Over the following years an immense amount of work was put into the detailed planning of a 1,380 bed hospital that was to stretch from Clarendon Road to Calverley Street. The scale of this project was truly breath-taking, for the site would have virtually covered an area corresponding to the ground between Park Row and the new Yorkshire Playhouse and between Boar Lane and the Headrow – ie the whole of the shopping centre of Leeds. Moreover, while the original Infirmary was built as a series of separate ward blocks two or three stories high, this building was to form one solid mass which, with underground parking for 1,400 cars, would have had seven floors. Had it been built, it would have been necessary to demolish the Womens' Hospital, the Medical School, the Dental School, the nurses' homes and the back of the Gilbert Scott building, but the Brotherton, Martin and Wellcome Wings (the last two then only four years old) would have been retained. The facade of the old Infirmary would have been left as a tiny relic on the front of this vast building. In the event this new hospital was to remain as a dream enshrined in the pages of the famous 'Grey Book', a substantial volume which detailed these elaborate plans (Fig. 6.1-4).

---

* This was not a new problem for in 1889 the Yorkshire College, with which the Medical School had amalgamated in 1884, expressed reservations about the purchase of the Mount Pleasant (old Medical School) site because it was not on the main Beech Grove estate.

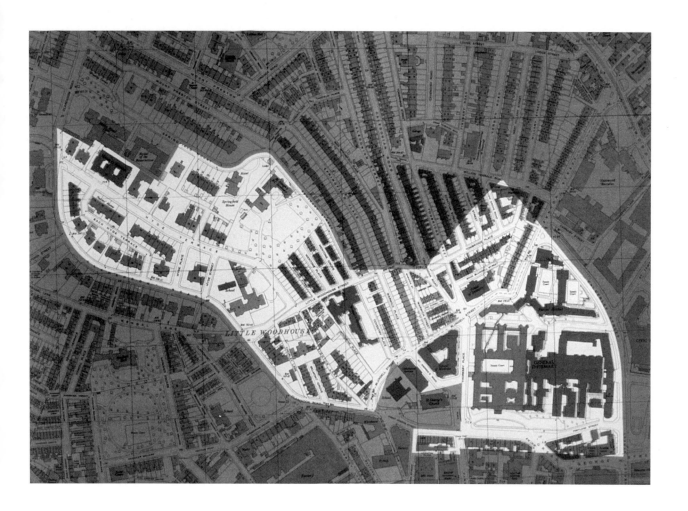

Fig. 6.1). *The site of the new hospital was to extend from Clarendon Road in the west to Calverley Street in the east and from the front of the old Playhouse to the middle of the existing Infirmary and Medical School. These last are visible on the right.*

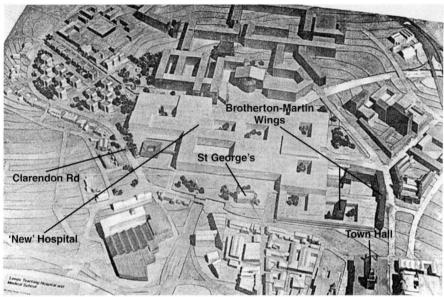

Fig.6.2). *A model of the 'new' hospital. Clarendon Road can be seen on the left and the Civic Hall is just beyond the dark-coloured buildings on the right – the relatively new Brotherton, Martin and Wellcome wings which were to be preserved.*

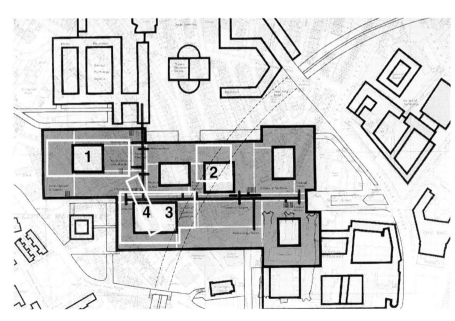

Fig. 6.3). *A map showing the size of the hospital planned and the size of the three buildings - Medical School (1), Generating station (2) and Clarendon Wing (3) - that were actually built. The Womens' Hospital lies under the upper part of the Clarendon Wing (4). The existing hospital buildings are in the bottom right hand corner.*

Problems

Those who read the Foreword to this 1965 publication carefully, however, could already sense trouble. It will be recalled that the Ministry and the University Grants Committee had 'agreed in principle to this expansion of the Leeds Schools (ie to 100 medical and 60 dental graduates per year) which is in line with accepted needs for more doctors and dentists in the next few decades'. But it now transpired that these bodies had subsequently 'asked the *University* (my italics) to consider increasing the number of medical students so that 150 rather than 100 graduate each year'. Worse still, the *University* (my italics) 'had agreed in principle to this request' but noted that 'if expansion to this size is to take place marked changes must occur in the concept of integrated teaching as set out in this Report'.

From the point of view of the Infirmary this was a sinister development. As the Teaching Hospital in Leeds it had been only too happy to participate in a joint development with the University. But its primary objective

Fig. 6.4). *A view showing the outline of the 'new' hospital building, on a site now largely cleared and bisected by the inner ring road. 1 = Gilbert Scott building; 2 = Womens' Hospital; 3 = Physiotherapy department; 4 = Inner ring road; 5 = Physics building.*

65

Fig.6.5). *At the onset, the Infirmary was still surrounded by a lot of old housing. This view was taken looking along Blundell St. on the north-west corner of the site. The Dental Hospital is on the left and hidden beyond it is the Department of Paediatrics (see Fig.6.8, 6.17). On the right is the Fenton St. Nurses' home. (Courtesy of the Leeds Library and Information Services).*

Fig. 6.6). *A view from the same position, but looking north towards the University. The Dental Hospital is visible in Tonbridge St. on the right and beyond that is the Tonbridge Hotel. On the left is Caledonian Rd. and the building between is the Physiotherapy Department. The car in the centre of the picture is a Jowett Javelin, which was made in Bradford.*

Fig. 6.7). *After clearance the Physiotherapy Department stands alone between the Dental Hospital and the Lipman Building.*

Fig. 6.8). *A view looking south-west down Blundell St. in about 1973, after extensive slum clearance. The new hospital was to have replaced the Nurses' Homes, the wards and much of the medical school on the left, the Dental School in the centre, the open area, the Womens' Hospital and the ground beyond and to the right. So far, the hospital had only gained a prodigious amount of parking space!*

had always been to build a new hospital, and if at this stage the University – whose idea it was – abandoned the concept of integration the whole project was in jeopardy. The new hospital had been designed, as agreed, to produce 100 graduates a year – a 35% increase on existing figures – but the number of beds could not be increased to train more. Yet the alternative proposed – that of establishing a second teaching centre elsewhere – violated every concept on which this vast project had been based. Faced with this dilemma the Board of the Faculty of Medicine reaffirmed its support for the plan as it stood. But the Senate, in what must be one of its most significant decisions ever, rejected this advice. It did however specify that expansion was conditional on 'adequate funds being available to safeguard quality' – an important proviso, for at that time grants were falling so far short of promises that, in the words of the Vice Chancellor, 'our building programme will be virtually at a standstill unless .....' Yet despite this the Senate was prepared to abandon its fundamental concept of all teaching taking place on one integrated site close to the University, abolish its special relationship with the Infirmary and propose the creation of a second Teaching Hospital in Leeds.

This decision, made by a body that had no responsibility for the provision of a hospital service, was a catastrophe for the Infirmary. For the sake of fifty extra students, years of preparation for a badly needed new hospital were thrown into turmoil and University and Ministry funds were diverted to St. James's – a large, neglected local authority hospital – to produce what the History of the Medical School describes as 'new buildings which are commodious, luxurious in parts' in a 'hospital that is quite transformed'. The practical consequences of this 'division of labour' were yet to become apparent.

This, however, was not the only problem, for having examined the plans the University Grants Committee also refused to sanction the full height 'service' floors which lay between each 'working' floor in that part of the new building designed for the Medical School*. Indeed between 1968 and 1971 it became apparent that the Department of Health and the University Grants Committee had decided to establish two separate contracts – one to accelerate the building of a *separated* Medical and Dental School designed (now) to produce *two* hundred students a year (half of whom were to be trained at St. James's) and the other for the first part of the Infirmary. The fundamental concept of all teaching taking place on one site in a fully integrated Medical Centre had therefore been abandoned and the plans for the new hospital were in ruins.

The appearance of the Medical School, a vast, bunker-like building nine floors in height, was not improved by the fact that it was built in concrete because the blue brick originally chosen was not available. Opened in 1977, it cost over eight million pounds and was sited so close to the Womens' Hospital that this much-loved building had to be demolished. Beside it stood a huge generating station and laundry, which cost a further four million pounds, designed to serve the whole of the 'new' hospital (Fig. 6.5-11). Its capacity was, of course, far in excess of any foreseeable need and it came to be known (after the unfortunate chairman who was grappling with what was rapidly becoming a fiasco) as Tweddle's Folly. It has indeed been suggested that, were it not for

---

* These floors, which can be seen when climbing the staircases in the Clarendon Wing, were inserted so that the function of any 'working' area could be altered with a minimum of difficulty.

Fig. 6.9). *A picture taken in April 1974 as work started on the new Medical School and the Generating Station. The building in the foreground is the Lipman building – the medical students' common room, named after the President of the Medical Student' Representative Council who negotiated for it but died before it was built. Beyond that are the inner ring road and the Hospital for Women.*

Fig. 6.10). *A picture taken in January 1975. The Hospital for Women has been demolished. The Generating Station is appearing on the right and the Medical and Dental School on the left. (The white building just to the left of the crane is a useful marker for comparison with 6.9).*

the embarrassment of having this huge, useless edifice on site, no further building would have taken place. Meantime the surplus energy was channelled into the National Grid. Indeed on one memorable occasion, during a brief but total breakdown of the power supply, it *became* the National Grid – thus activating alarms throughout the hospital!

Retrenchment

The Infirmary was now in a precarious situation. After years of preparation, the University had completely altered the brief on which the partnership was based and abandoned its exclusive link with the Hospital. For the University this was not a major issue, for modifying its plans for the Medical School was a relatively simple process. Redesigning a major hospital in the face of rising costs, a worsening economic situation and the diversion of resources to develop St. James's was an entirely different matter.

The entire project might, indeed, have foundered but for two things. With the demolition of the Women's Hospital the gynaecologists had been 'temporarily' marooned in a mansion in Roundhay. Meantime a vast, useless generating station steamed merrily in the midst of a large area of total desolation. Under such circumstances, it was evident that something had to be done. A second, much modified plan was therefore produced at the end of 1968. This envisaged that work on the first phase of a new hospital would begin in 1971 and be completed in 1976 (Fig. 6.12,13). Second, third and fourth phases would be completed in 1978, 1981 and

Fig. 6.11). *The Medical and Dental School and the Generating Station, which occupy the upper part of the site, seen through the gap between the Lipman Building and the Dental Hospital.*

70

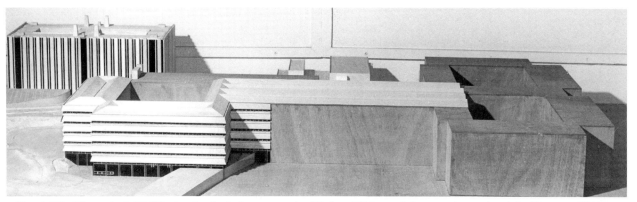

Fig. 6.12). *The revised (1968) plan for the Infirmary received little publicity, and there are few copies of the diagrams. This one shows the Clarendon Wing in front of the new Medical School on the left with the second (central) and third (right) phases that were never built. Two stories have been removed from the original plan and the area occupied by the Medical School and Generating Station have, of course, been lost.*

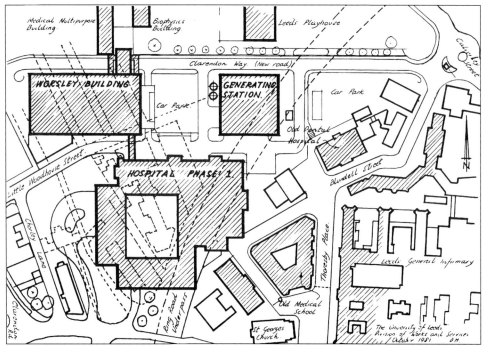

Fig 6.13). *The first phase of the revised plan. Note how the Clarendon Wing overlies the site of the Hospital for Women and the distance between the new building and the Infirmary.*

71

1984 at an overall cost of twenty-five million pounds. In the event it was December 1972 before the foundation stone was laid in the garden of the old Womens' Hospital and in 1977 (by which time the estimated cost of the first phase had risen to £11.7 million) the 300 bed building still only existed as an architect's model. It was 1984 before this part of the 'new Infirmary', which alone cost twenty-five million pounds, was opened. It was to be the last.

The final irony, however, was that this coincided with a report from a Department of Health working party on medical manpower to the effect that the number of medical students needed to be substantially *reduced* and that there was a case for closing one of the country's medical schools. (Times 11.2.1984). The implementation of the original plan for the new hospital had therefore been prevented by a national demand for *more* students who, it now transpired, were no longer needed!

The Clarendon Wing

The 'first phase' of the 'new hospital' *was* built, but was designed with the utmost economy. The freestanding car-park, essential for the smooth running of clinics in this congested corner of the city, was removed from the plan along with one of the floors, and the foundations were so modified that they could not be restored at a later date. It was moreover made abundantly clear that units could only move in on a 'level transfer' basis (ie that they must cost no more on the new site than on the old) and that additional services would only be funded if, after close scrutiny, it had been confirmed that they were 'inextricably and unavoidably associated

Fig. 6.14). *The Clarendon Wing site in August 1977, seen from the new Medical School. The Algernon Firth building, the old Medical School, the Lipman Building and the Infirmary can be seen beyond the long pale block that encloses the inner ring road.*

with bringing essential new facilities into use'. As a result large parts of the building stood empty and, for many years, 'planning' meant discussing how these 'advance structures' (skeletal concrete caverns) could best be used. The intensity of the prevailing economy is perhaps best illustrated by the fact that when the roof of Ward 2 of the Gilbert Scott building was damaged in a gale, it was only repaired after the medical staff had prepared and presented a detailed statistical analysis of the consequences of leaving the ward out of action.

By the same token, the new block might well have been planned as a protest against the opulence of the Victorian Infirmary. Squat and devoid of character or adornment, it appears to have very few windows. In place of well lit, airy corridors it has an endless succession of featureless, fully enclosed tunnels that leave the uninformed visitor with no idea of where he is or which way he is going. Many of the innumerable offices are minute and the wards – evidently the main feature of the old Infirmary – are hard to find. But the most amazing difference is the way in which the wards are deployed *along* the sides of the building – a layout that restores the very defects which the old Infirmary was designed to abolish. This of course means that the windows, which are small and shielded, only run down one side. The innermost beds are therefore poorly illuminated, and the occupants spend much of their time looking into the glare of overhead lights (Fig. 6.14-16). In place of the side-to-side ventilation for which the Nightingale wards were renowned, many of the beds in the Clarendon wing lie in a draught that flows between the main doors from the corridor and the windows. And while the sluices of the old Infirmary were isolated in projections at the ends of the wards, at least one side ward in the Clarendon Wing appears to be separated by a flimsy panel from a heavily used lavatory.

Fig. 6.15). *The Clarendon Wing. Note the size of the windows, the screening and the size of the car park. The new Medical School can be seen on the left.*

Fig. 6.16). *A ward area in the Clarendon Wing before 'fitting out'. The low ceiling and the lack of natural light and ventilation are immediately apparent.*

Fig. 6.17). *A view taken from the same position as 6.8 after the building of the Clarendon Wing. The Department of Paediatrics (the house) is still intact and beyond that the Generating Station, the new Medical School and the bridge linking it with the Clarendon Wing can be seen. The old Nurses' Home is on the left – and with the demolition of the Dental Hospital the car parks are still proliferating. This area is now occupied by the Jubilee Wing (see back cover).*

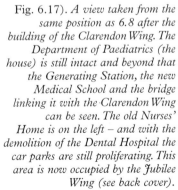

The problem of access is even more serious. Entry from the old Hospital, which is a quarter of a mile away, involved a long, complicated journey through the 'snake' – a sloping 'tunnel on stilts' that began near the court-yard and wound its way round the Medical School and the Algernon Firth Building. For the elderly and infirm, for doctors attending emergencies and for patients being moved between the intensive care unit and the neuro x-ray department this was a formidable obstacle. For those who were able bodied entry from the Medical School was easier although, because floor levels no longer matched, it still involved coming down a steep flight of stairs to a landing between the 6th. and 7th. floors (Fig. 17-19). But the biggest problem is that of that of getting access to the main entrance. This lies at the end of a narrow tortuous road which branches off a bend at the bottom of a steep hill. There is virtually no public transport in the vicinity and (with the loss of the planned car-park) virtually no parking. Many of those attending the clinics, who often have defective vision, are pregnant or are accompanied by children, are therefore unable to reach the hospital without the aid of a lift, a taxi or an ambulance. It was, of course, a problem which was anticipated in the 1965 plan, but the large car-park incorporated to deal with it was removed 'in the interests of economy'.

The Jubilee Wing

For the next ten years the hospital was precariously linked to the Clarendon Wing by this unsightly umbilical cord and surrounded by the collection of unplanned car-parks and rickety buildings left by the slum clearance (Fig. 6.17). Then, in 1993, plans for a new Phase I began to appear. By now, however, all thought of

Fig. 6.18). *'The Snake' that linked the Infirmary to the Clarendon Wing. To the left is the octagonal Anatomy Lecture Theatre of the old Medical School. On the right is the Lipman Building.*

Fig. 6.19). *Aerial view of the site as it was for ten years between the building of the Clarendon and Jubilee Wings. Note the vast 'car parks' produced by slum clearance in anticipation of the 1965 plan. 1 = Medical school; 2 = Clarendon wing; 3 = Generating station; 4 = 'The snake'; 5 = old Nurses' Home; 6 = Fenton St. Wing; 7 = Stables home; 8 = Edward VII Home; 9 = Sunny Bank Home; 10 = 1892 block; 11 = Wellcome wing; 12 = 'tower' from 1892 outpatient' block; 13 = 1917 block; 14 = Brotherton wing; 15 = Martin wing.*

76

developing a self contained hospital had gone, and each of the two teaching hospitals had resorted to a policy of enticing prestigious departments to centralise on its own site. With all its defects, there were good reasons for this approach. The increasing cost and complexity of modern medicine means that neither institution can afford or house fully equipped units for every speciality. By the same token, restrictions on the hours for which junior doctors are allowed to work mean that it is no longer possible to duplicate every department. Instead, for good or ill, some specialities are concentrated in one hospital and some in the other.

Where the Infirmary was concerned, this meant a new eighty million pound building designed to accommodate neurosurgical services (including those from Pinderfields), cardiothoracic services (including those from Killingbeck), a large new Accident and Emergency department (with a helipad) and a new x-ray department. Among the facilities provided were fourteen new theatres, sixteen x-ray suites and thirty-five intensive care beds. At one stage there was even talk of converting the old Nurses' Home into a hotel for the benefit of relatives! Clearance of the site, which involved the demolition of the old Dental Hospital, began in 1994 and at one stage, when the wall of the Inner Ring Road was exposed, an office on one corner of the Clarendon Wing appeared to be propped up on a pile of bricks. By 1997, however, the new building – which links the Clarendon Wing with the Infirmary – was complete (Fig. 6.20-24).

There is a striking contrast between the size, style and planning of the old Infirmary and the Jubilee Wing. In particular the latter has again abandoned the Nightingale wards, originally introduced to control the

Fig. 6.20). *Site clearance for the Jubilee Wing, 1994. Moving from the left one can see the Clarendon Wing, the multi-storey car park, the Fenton St. Nurses' Home, the end of the old Nurses' Home, the corner of the Infirmary and the remains of the 'snake'.*

Fig. 6.21). *The wall of the inner ring road exposed during preparation of the site for the Jubilee Wing, with one corner of a Clarendon Wing office precariously propped up.*

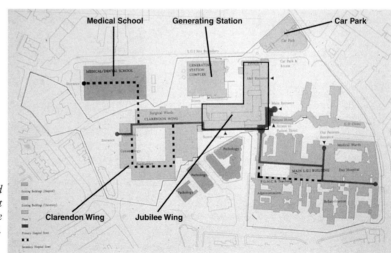

Fig. 6.22). *A diagram to show how the 'reversed L' of the Jubilee Wing joins the Gilbert Scott building in the bottom right with the square Clarendon Wing on the left.*

Fig. 6.23). *View of the new building looking up Thoresby Place between the old Medical School on the left and the Infirmary on the right – the view seen on 6.6 and 6.7.*

Fig. 6.24). *The link with the Jubilee Building as seen looking west across the back of the Infirmary. The north-west ward block is on the left.*

hospital infections that are once more becoming a problem. But there are also interesting links between the two. Both have the same light, airy corridors and the medicinal plants on the stone corbels in the hall of the Infirmary are echoed in wood-carvings in the lobby of the new wing (Fig. 6.25). Most interesting of all, however, is the physical link between the buildings, which was created by 'gutting' the ward block on the north west corner of the Infirmary and running a ramp up from the corridor round the courtyard, through the end window and into the new lobby. This allows the visitor to see the structure of the old Nightingale wards with their terminal sluices and, as he goes through the 'window', to admire exquisite stonework which, for over a hundred years, has been barely noticed (Fig. 6.26-29). Access to the new building, happily, is much improved, for there is a good entrance near well-signed major roads, a multi-storey car park and public transport within walking distance. Above all, after twenty-five years the Infirmary, if not rebuilt or entire, is at least again in one piece.

Fig. 6.25). *Carving in the lobby of the Jubilee Wing which, like the corbels in the front hall of the Infirmary (Fig. 2.23) depicts plants used in medicine.*

Fig. 6.26). *The link is via the rather unattractive central window on the ground floor, once the window of a sluice.*

Figs. 6.27, 28). *Closer examination shows that this entrance is surrounded by some fine (and hitherto neglected) stonework which has become an elegant framework for the doorway.*

Fig. 6.28.

Fig. 6.29). *The interior of the two wards in the north west corner has been entirely stripped and replaced by ramps that run up from the corridor round the central courtyard to the new entrance lobby. The arch at the far end is the interior of the window shown on 6.26-28. Note also the paired alcoves - once lavatories and bathrooms - at that end of the block.*

Fig. 6.30). *Carnaby St., 1913. This street, which was on the line of Calverley St. between the end of the Edward VII home and the roundabout outside the Jubilee Wing is typical of the vast areas of housing cleared to build and extend the Infirmary. (By courtesy of the Leeds Libraries and Information Services).*

7 – Reappraisal

IT IS INTERESTING TO review the consequences of the Senate's fateful decision in the light of subsequent events. Plainly neither party got what it set out to achieve, for the Medical School is not a single institution, is not an integral part of *the* Teaching Hospital and (to a large extent) is not in close proximity to the University. The new Infirmary, which even on the revised plan should have been completed by 1984, was never built. Worst of all, the plans for a new hospital were aborted because of a demand for more students when, within twenty years, it was decided that numbers should be reduced. As a result, forty years after the inception of the scheme large parts of the Gilbert Scott building – now 130 years old – are still in regular use.

Could things, and *should* things have been otherwise? In the financial climate of the 1960's, with the enthusiastic support of Ministry, Hospital and University, there was certainly a 'window of opportunity' to build this great new hospital. But 'mega hospitals' elsewhere have been difficult to run, and freedom from competition and massive bidding power for funds make them hard to control. There are also obvious dangers in concentrating all services in one place, lest the institution be the scene of a serious accident or outbreak of infection. But above all, one wonders if this immense building would have 'worked'. It was, after all, the very antithesis of the Gilbert Scott hospital with its two or three storey ward blocks surrounded by light and air. Could reasonable working conditions have been sustained at the heart of this vast seven-storey edifice with a few small courtyards and air conditioning – a device which, at that time, had not proved to be a notable success elsewhere?

There is, however, another aspect to the problem – an aspect which, in all fairness, the planners of the 1960's would have needed amazing wisdom to anticipate. It stems from the way in which hospital medicine – its organisation and working hours and the cost of its equipment – has been transformed over the last four decades. Hitherto the essential feature of a hospital had been its beds and its disciplined, dedicated, highly experienced nursing staff. On the medical side, individual wards were run by 'firms', each of which was largely self-sufficient and provided constant medical cover for its own patients through the medium of 'residents' who rarely left the building. The day-to-day management of the unit was in the hands of registrars – men with a wide experience of medicine and a sound knowledge of the subject in which their 'chief' had a particular interest. The consultant staff, most of whom – at least in theory – were *general* physicians or surgeons, visited regularly to give advice, to hold clinics, to operate or to teach, but the institution could and did run smoothly in their absence. Above all, even in the 1960s, there was little in the way of expensive equipment.

Over recent years, this well-established situation has been transformed. At the simplest level, the cost of much of the specialised equipment has become so great that it is clearly unreasonable to provide and maintain it on two adjacent sites. Yet without such equipment a 'centre of excellence' cannot provide a clinical service, train junior staff or carry out research. The problem of staffing is even more complex. Junior staff, who once provided constant supervision, are now forbidden to work more than one night in five. This makes it difficult for individual specialities to provide adequate round-the-clock cover on one, let alone two sites and deprives the junior staff of the vast clinical experience that was formerly the essence of their training. As a result registrars – who at one time could work independently – are increasingly obliged to look to the consultant staff for advice and help. But no provision has been made for a one-in-five rota for consultants, and older men in small specialities can hardly be expected to turn out night after night to assist juniors whose off-duty time is protected. Moreover many consultants, being forced by the complexity of their subjects* to concentrate on one speciality or even one sub-speciality, no longer even pretend to be *general* physicians or surgeons. A gulf has therefore emerged between less experienced registrars on the one hand and consultants with narrow interests on the other. To provide a truly comprehensive service all specialties would therefore have to be represented at all levels and at all times on both sites.

This approach, unfortunately, would dilute the clinical experience of both hospitals, would lead to the wasteful duplication of expensive equipment and would be an inefficient way of using both senior and junior medical staff. Instead, a policy of 'division of labour' has been adopted, whereby only one or other hospital is fully equipped and staffed to deal with certain problems. But, as the great specialist hospitals in London found many years ago, medicine cannot be sub-divided in this way, for in a special centre the neurological patient who goes into diabetic coma or the orthopaedic patient who develops renal failure is in very real danger. The same must apply to a hospital service which is divided between two sites. It is not a pattern designed to produce 'excellence'.

Yet this, sadly, is the dilemma with which Leeds is now faced, for neither of its two great hospitals has the space, the money or the staff to run a comprehensive service. It is a dilemma which, at least in theory, the 1965 plan would have avoided, for it would have produced a modern building in which all services were represented. There would not therefore have been any wasteful duplication of expensive equipment, the organisation of rotas for each speciality would have been facilitated and experts in every field would always have been available. It would have been a building in which, because of the interleaved service floors, the function of any given area could be changed with a minimum of difficulty. Moreover, it was a building whose vast flat roof provided an unrivalled area for further development. Was it right to sacrifice this opportunity for the sake of fifty students, when students were already being taught in surrounding hospitals? If a second teaching hospital *was* required, would it not have been more sensible to place it in, say, Hull or Bradford? And if the University Hospital of St. James can function in isolation, was there any need to insist that the Infirmary should be rebuilt in the centre of an increasingly congested city? We will never know.

---

* and indeed by the demands of their patients and the Royal Colleges.